The **Mice** and the **Elephants**

by Chitra Soundar and Aditi Kakade Beaufrand

W
FRANKLIN WATTS
LONDON•SYDNEY

In an old house in a forest, there lived some mice.

Every day, the mice ran along the path.

At the end of the path there was a lake.

The lake was always full of cool, clear water

for the mice to drink.

Then one day, a herd of elephants
came looking for water.
Geya, the leader of the elephants,
walked in front.
The elephants did not see the little mice
on the path.

"Danger!" cried Moosha, the leader of the mice.

"Quickly, get off the path or we will be trampled."

The mice scampered off the path.

The elephants drank the water.

Then they washed themselves in the lake.

"This is a wonderful lake," said Geya.

"We will come here every day."

So, every day the elephants came along

the path to the lake, and every day

the mice scampered off the path

so they would not be trampled.

Then one day, Moosha said, "I am
fed up of being scared. I am going to
talk to the elephants about this."
"The elephants are so big," said the mice.
"Why would they listen to a little mouse
like you?"
"We may be little," said Moosha, "but we
can still be friends with elephants."

So, Moosha set off to see the elephants.

"I am Moosha, the leader of the mice," he said.

Geya looked down at Moosha.

"I am Geya, the leader of the herd," she said. "What do you want?"

"Every day you come down the path to the lake," said Moosha. "You do not see us and we have to scamper away so we do not get trampled. Please will you go another way to the lake?"

Geya was surprised. "I am very sorry," she said. "We are so big that we did not see you on the path. We did not mean to frighten you. We will go another way to the lake."

"Thank you," said Moosha, "you are a good friend."

"Yes," said Geya, "friends can be big or small, but they always help each other."

So, the elephants went a different way to the lake and the mice were safe. Everyone was happy.

Until the day when the hunter came.

The hunter looked at Geya. "The king

will pay a good price for such

a big elephant," he thought.

That night, the hunter dug a large pit.

He covered the pit with leaves and sticks.

The trap was ready.

The next day, the elephants came to the lake.

"THUD!"

Geya fell into the pit.

The hunter and his men pulled Geya out
and tied her to the trees.

"We will come back tomorrow,"
said the hunter. "Then we can take her
to the king."

Geya tugged at the ropes but they were stron

Geya trumpeted loudly.

From inside his house, Moosha heard

Geya's call.

16

"Our friend is in danger," he said.

The mice rushed to the forest. They found
Geya tied to the tree.

"Don't worry," said Moosha. "We'll free you."

The mice bit the ropes with their teeth.

Soon the ropes broke and Geya was free.

"Thank you. You're a good friend,"

said Geya.

"Yes, friends can be big or small," said Moosha, "but they always help each other."

Story order

Look at these 5 pictures and captions.
Put the pictures in the right order
to retell the story.

1

Geya calls to the mice for help.

2

The elephants do not see the mice.

3

Geya thanks her friend Moosha.

4

Moosha visits the elephants.

5

Geya falls into a hunter's trap.

Independent Reading

This series is designed to provide an opportunity for your child to read on their own. These notes are written for you to help your child choose a book and to read it independently.

In school, your child's teacher will often be using reading books which have been banded to support the process of learning to read. Use the book band colour your child is reading in school to help you make a good choice. *The Mice and the Elephants* is a good choice for children reading at Purple Band in their classroom to read independently.

The aim of independent reading is to read this book with ease, so that your child enjoys the story and relates it to their own experiences.

About the book

In this retelling of a famous Indian tale, the mice are nearly trampled by elephants on the path to the lake. Moosha, leader of the mice, asks the elephants to watch out for the mice. One day, the head elephant, Geya, falls into a hunter's trap and the mice come to the rescue.

Before reading

Help your child to learn how to make good choices by asking: "Why did you choose this book? Why do you think you will enjoy it?" Look at the cover together and ask: "What do you think the story will be about?" Ask your child to think of what they already know about the story context. Then ask your child to read the title aloud. Ask: "What are some of the main differences between the two animals?" Remind your child that they can sound out the letters to make a word if they get stuck.

Decide together whether your child will read the story independently or read it aloud to you.

During reading

Remind your child of what they know and what they can do independently. If reading aloud, support your child if they hesitate or ask for help by telling the word. If reading to themselves, remind your child that they can come and ask for your help if stuck.

After reading

Support comprehension by asking your child to tell you about the story. Use the story order puzzle to encourage your child to retell the story in the right sequence, in their own words. The correct sequence can be found on the next page.

Help your child think about the messages in the book that go beyond the story and ask: "Why do you think Moosha wanted to be friends with the elephants? What do do you think both sets of animals have learned at the end?"

Give your child a chance to respond to the story: "How do you think Moosha felt when visiting the elephants? How did Moosha return Geya's kindness?"

Extending learning

Help your child predict other possible outcomes of the story by asking: "What do you think would happen if the mice had been too scared to ask the elephants to go a different way to the lake?"
In the classroom, your child's teacher may be teaching how to use speech marks when characters are speaking. There are many examples in this book that you could look at with your child. Find these together and point out how the end punctuation (comma, full stop, question mark or exclamation mark) comes inside the speech marks. Ask the child to read some examples out loud, adding appropriate expression.

Franklin Watts
First published in Great Britain in 2021
by The Watts Publishing Group

Series Editors: Jackie Hamley and Melanie Palmer
Series Advisors and Development Editors: Dr Sue Bodman and Glen Franklin
Series Designers: Peter Scoulding and Cathryn Gilbert

A CIP catalogue record for this book is
available from the British Library.

ISBN 978 1 4451 7690 1(hbk)
ISBN 978 1 4451 7692 5 (pbk)
ISBN 978 1 4451 8191 2 (ebook)
ISBN 978 1 4451 7691 8 (library ebook)

Printed in China

Franklin Watts
An imprint of
Hachette Children's Group
Part of The Watts Publishing Group
Carmelite House
50 Victoria Embankment
London EC4Y 0DZ

An Hachette UK Company
www.hachette.co.uk

www.franklinwatts.co.uk

Answer to Story order: 2,4,5,1,3